G000128405

Many people believe that they can't do maths or t
refresh your maths and remind you that maths c

Junior Maths Medicine gives junior school children and their parents the chance to work together on the kind of maths that features in the National Numeracy Strategy.

The key to solving the questions in this book is to find a sensible meaning for the mathematical ideas involved. Give yourself plenty of time and discuss your ideas with family or friends. Don't worry if you go wrong. It's a step nearer going right.

The Maths Medicine website, at **www.mathsmed.co.uk**, shows some of the methods readers have used. You can send your methods and comments to Professor Smudge by writing to Dexter Graphics, or by using the online report form, or by sending an email to **smudge@mathsmed.co.uk**.

The Maths Medicine website provides help and answers. There is also a brief answers section at the back of this book.

(D)

Junior
Maths Medicine®

Published in the UK by

Dexter Graphics, 119 St James's Drive, London SW17 7RP

tel/fax   020 8767 4319   email   info@mathsmed.co.uk

© Dexter Graphics 1999   First Published 1999   Reprinted 2003

All rights reserved. No part of this publication may be reproduced in any material form (including photocopying or storing it in any medium by electronic means and whether or not transiently or incidentally to some other use of this publication) without the written permission of the copyright owner except in accordance with the provisions of the Copyright, Designs and Patents Act 1988 or under the terms of a licence issued by the Copyright Licensing Agency, 90 Tottenham Court Road, London, W1P 0LP. Applications for the copyright owner's written permission to reproduce any part of this publication should be addressed to the publisher.

Warning: The doing of an unauthorised act in relation to a copyright work may result in both a civil claim for damages and criminal prosecution.

Design, illustrations and typesetting by Dexter Graphics
Printed in China by Nordica Printing Co (Panyu) Ltd

ISBN 0-9534035-2-1

Also available

Maths Medicine (3 months' supply of daily maths items for the general reader)   ISBN 0953403505
Mini Maths Medicine (2 weeks' supply of maths items for the general reader)   ISBN 0953403513

A cup of tea costs 95p.

What is the smallest number of
coins needed to pay for it exactly?

Paulo divides 298.2 by 9.15 on his calculator.
He gets these digits in the display.

Where does the decimal point go?

The shape is folded to make a box without a top.

Which square is the base of the box?

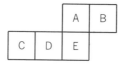

When it is 9 am in London
it is 5 pm in Tokyo, Japan.

What is the time in London
when it is 9 am in Tokyo?

What is the smallest possible
digit under this ink blot?

$$
\begin{array}{r}
6\, \bullet \\
+\ 2\, 6 \\
\hline
9\, \bullet
\end{array}
$$

The 20th pattern has 210 dots.

How many dots does the 21st pattern have?

1st   2nd   3rd   4th

Nisha buys 5 bottles of
water for a camping trip.
She drinks $\frac{1}{4}$ of one bottle.

What fraction of her water
supply has she drunk?

Do you think there is anyone still alive who was born more than 1000 months ago?

The shapes are made from 1 cm squares.
The perimeter of shape A is 12 cm.

What is the perimeter of shape B ?

A 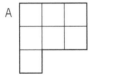 B

Some counters are arranged to make a 26 by 17 rectangle.

Name another rectangle that can be made from all the counters.

The calculation is correct.

How can this be possible?

$$
\begin{array}{r}
2.34 \\
+\ 1.45 \\
\hline
4.19
\end{array}
$$

Card E is coloured red on the back.
Lisa wants to place the card exactly on top of card F.

Will the red side or the blue side be visible?

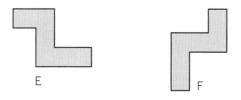

E

F

The drawing shows how Ashley shares a cake with Brenda and Clare (the bit left over is for the dog).

What fraction of the cake does each person get?

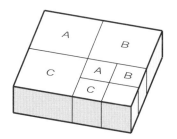

If January the 1st is a Saturday,
what day is January the 31st ?

How much does a box of
two hundred 19p stamps cost?

Which numbers have the larger average,
those in set A or those in set B ?

A: 16, 7, 19, 11, 62, 5

B: 16, 7, 19, 11, 62

A shop sells the same rice
in different packs, P and Q.

Which pack is the better value?

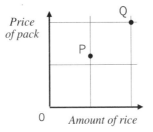

Think of the 100th tile in this pattern.

Is it the same as the 1st, 2nd, or 3rd tile?

A ladder is 2000 __ long.

What could the missing unit be?

A ball costs £17.49.

How much change do you get if
you pay only with 20p coins?

The largest factor of 652 is 652.

What is the next largest factor?

Tim has 10p more than Jez.
They have 98p altogether.

How much does Tim have?

The scale shows the weight of a parcel, in kg.

Roughly, what does the parcel weigh in grams?

Bill uses his calculator to find 3×294.
He presses a wrong key for one of the digits
and gets the result 1182 instead of 882.

What was his actual calculation?

The 50th term of this sequence is 148.

1, 4, 7, 10, 13, 16, 19, ...

Find the 60th term.

A 15 mm wide marble just fits
inside the cube–shaped box.

How many 5 mm wide marbles
could fit inside the box?

Find a simpler division that gives the same result as

$$30 \div 2\frac{1}{2}.$$

The number 9254 is divisible by 7.

Do you think it is also divisible by 14 ?

M is the midpoint of AB and YZ.

What kind of quadrilateral is AZBY ?

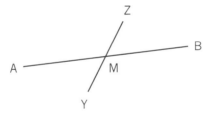

Is the beaker 35 %, 45 %, 55 % or 65 % full?

A tortoise walks 1.3 metres.
It moves forward another 2 mm.

How far has it travelled
altogether, in metres?

In this multiplication, 5 digits are covered by pieces of card.

$$3\boxed{A} \times 1\boxed{B} = \boxed{C}\boxed{D}\boxed{E}$$

What is the largest possible digit under card C ?

The shape is made from 1 cm squares. Its perimeter is 38 cm.

The blue square is removed. What is the perimeter of the shape that is left?

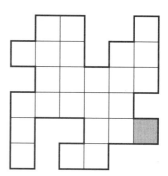

Uma only has 8p and 12p stamps.
She can make a total of £1 by using
eleven 8p stamps and one 12p stamp.

In how many other ways can
she make a total of £1 ?

The average of 8, 10 and 21 is 13.

What is the average of 8, 10, 21 and 13 ?

Find the missing prime number.

41,   43,   47,   __,   59

AB, BC and CD are straight lines.

AB is perpendicular to BC.

BC is perpendicular to CD.

What can you say about AB and CD ?

Add 0.0001 and 5.939999

The number pyramid starts with the numbers 2, 3 and 7. It produces 14.

What is the largest number that a pyramid starting with 2, 3 and 7 can produce?

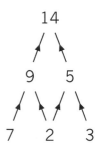

The graph can be used to convert pounds to Australian dollars and New Zealand dollars.

Which is worth more, an Australian or a New Zealand dollar?

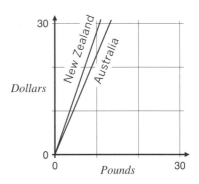

Put these in order, smallest first.

$$\frac{1}{5} \qquad 0.5 \qquad 5\,\%$$

Terry chooses two of these
numbers and multiplies them.

1.98   2.98   3.98   4.98   5.98   6.98

The result is 17.8204.

Which numbers did Terry choose?

The dots are spaced 1 cm apart.

Find the area of the square.

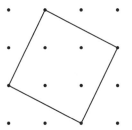

The minute hand of a clock turns 120°.

How many degrees does the hour hand turn?

Fay's number is 1 smaller than Daryl's.
They both divide their number by 3.
Fay gets a remainder of 2.

What remainder does Daryl get?

These calculations give
the same answer:

$923 - 65$ and $N - 100$.

What is the value of N ?

A class of 30 children takes a
reading test and a writing test.

Which test was easier?

	fail	pass
pass	8	9
fail	7	6

READING (pass / fail rows)

WRITING (fail / pass columns)

£1 is worth €1.5.

What is €1 worth, in pence?

16 counters are arranged to make
a 6 counter by 4 counter border.

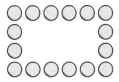

How many counters are needed for
a 20 counter by 5 counter border?

A bowl contains 3 apples.
One of the apples weighs 160 g
and another weighs 170 g.

What can you say about
the 3rd apple if the mean
weight of the apples is
more than 170 g ?

The number 15 has 4 factors:

1,   3,   5,   15.

Find a larger number with 4 factors.

Find the temperature that is
midway between ⁻6 °C and 10 °C.

Fiona is building a 3 cm cube from 1 cm cubes.

How many more 1 cm cubes does she need?

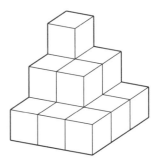

Oleg spins one of the spinners
12 times and adds the scores.
He wants a high total score.

Which spinner should he choose?

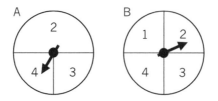

A

2

4   3

B

1   2

4   3

50 identical paper clips weigh
14 grams, to the nearest gram.

What could 49 paper clips weigh,
to the nearest gram?

529 1 cm square tiles are needed to cover a 23 cm square.

How many *extra* 1 cm tiles are needed for a 24 cm square?

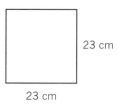

23 cm

23 cm

$299 \times 10 = 2990,$

so $299 \times 9 =$ ___.

Which is larger, the number of seconds in a day, or the number of minutes in a week?

JUNE						
M	T	W	T	F	S	S
			1	2	3	4
5	6	7	8	9	10	11
12	13	14	15	16	17	18
19	20	21	22	23	24	25
26	27	28	29	30		

Janice eats a bowl of cornflakes for breakfast.

Estimate the number of cornflakes that she eats.
Choose from these numbers:

20   200   2000   20 000   200 000

There are 30 children and a teacher in a room.

Which do you think is larger, the mean age or
the median age of the people in the room?

Which arrow, P, Q or R, points to 5.09 ?

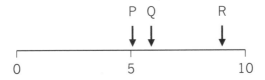

This is a solid cube made from blue cubes and white cubes, placed alternately.

How many more blue cubes are there than white cubes?

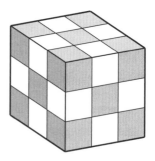

$2 * 8 = 15$ and $10 * 3 = 29$.

What is the value of $9 * 5$?

Points A, B and C are vertices of a rectangle.

Find the coordinates of the fourth vertex.

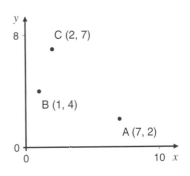

How many dots does the 8th pattern have?

1st   2nd   3rd

What is "half of one percent" as a fraction?

A sheet of A4 paper measures 21 cm by 29.7 cm.

Martin has 22 sheets of A4 paper.
Is this enough to cover a 1 metre square?

Emmy and Karim are mixing
blue paint and yellow paint to make green.

Emmy mixes 2 jars of blue with 3 jars of yellow paint.
Karim mixes 8 jars of blue with 9 jars of yellow paint.

Whose colour is more yellowy, or do they look the same?

Is the angle less than, equal to, or greater than 115° ?

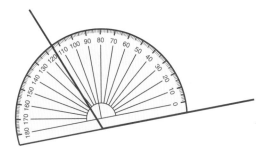

$526 \times 21 = 11\ 046.$

Calculate 536×21.

Find the perimeter of the rectangle.

$5 + n$

$5 - n$

The graph is for Sofia's
marks on 28 spelling tests.

Is her average mark less than,
equal to, or more than 3 ?

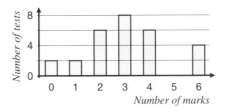

$2 \times 3 \times 11 = 66.$

So 2, 3, and 11
are factors of 66,
as are 1 and 66.

Find the other
factors of 66.

A kitten is 0.14 years old.

Roughly how old will it
be in 1 week's time?

The numbers 7, 8 and 9 are consecutive.
Their sum is 24.

Find three consecutive numbers whose sum is 147.

Find a fraction that lies somewhere between $\frac{1}{5}$ and $\frac{2}{5}$.

A bell rings every 7 minutes.
It rings at exactly 2 pm.

When next does it ring
exactly on the hour?

DING!

The point P has coordinates (50, 100) and is on the line *m*.

Another point has coordinates (19, 40). Is it on line *m*, or in region A, or in region B ?

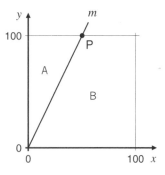

Two of these cards are placed side by side
to make a 2 digit number (for example 25).

| 2 | 3 | 5 | 6 |

How many different 2 digit numbers
can be made with the cards?

Does 141 belong to this sequence?

8,   15,   22,   29,   36,   ...

One gallon is 8 pints.
A pint of water weighs 20 oz.
16 oz is 1 lb.

Find the weight of a gallon
of water, in lb.

A pile of 100 sheets of paper is 1.03 cm thick.

Roughly how thick is a pile of 101 sheets?

Sherri earns £450 per week
and spends 15 % of this on rent.
Cath earns £190 per week and
spends 28 % of this on rent.

Who pays more rent?

The drawing shows part of a very tall triangle.

What is the size of the hidden angle?

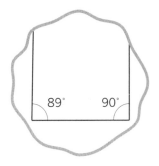

89° 90°

How much larger is 26 plus twice 29
than 29 plus twice 26 ?

Is $\frac{1}{50}$ nearer to $\frac{1}{10}$ or to $\frac{1}{100}$?

You roll two dice.
Which is more likely, result X or result Y ?

X: You get a 3 on at least one of the dice.

Y: You get a total of 3 on the two dice.

The diagram is for the factors of 250.

Which factor is missing?

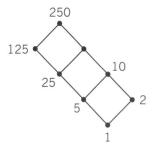

250

125

25

10

5

2

1

The average age of the 11 players
in a hockey team is 9 years 2 months.

The average age of the players and
their manager is 10 years 2 months.

How old is the manager?

Ed is walking at a speed
of 50 metres per minute.
Bruno is 100 metres behind
Ed and walking at a speed
of 100 metres per minute.

How many minutes does it take
Bruno to catch up with Ed?

Which is larger, $21 \div 5$ or $21.1 \div 5.1$?

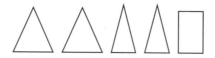

The five pieces of card can be fitted
together to make a closed pyramid.

Is it possible to make a closed pyramid
with just the triangular pieces?

ANSWERS

When you are working on a question, don't turn to the answer too soon. The answers have been kept brief and fuller answers can be found on the Maths Medicine website, at **www.mathsmed.co.uk**. The site provides help and explanations, as well as methods used by readers. The site is updated regularly and Professor Smudge is pleased to receive your methods and comments. You can contact Professor Smudge by writing to Dexter Graphics, or by using the online report form, or by sending an email to **smudge@mathsmed.co.uk**.

DAY 1 4.　　**DAY 2** between the 2 and the 5.　　**DAY 3** A.　　**DAY 4** 1 am.　　**DAY 5** 4.　　**DAY 6** 231.

DAY 7 $\frac{1}{20}$.　　**DAY 8** yes.　　**DAY 9** 12 cm.　　**DAY 10** 13 by 34 (or 2 by 221, or 1 by 442).

DAY 11 the numbers could stand for hours and minutes, or minutes and seconds.　　**DAY 12** blue.

DAY 13 $\frac{5}{16}$.　　**DAY 14** Monday.　　**DAY 15** £38.　　**DAY 16** B.　　**DAY 17** Q.　　**DAY 18** 1st.

DAY 19 mm.　　**DAY 20** 11p.　　**DAY 21** 326.　　**DAY 22** 54p.　　**DAY 23** ≈ 370 g.　　**DAY 24** 3×394.

DAY 25 178.　　**DAY 26** 27.　　**DAY 27** for example, $60 \div 5$ (or $120 \div 10$).　　**DAY 28** yes.

DAY 29 a parallelogram.　　**DAY 30** 35 %.　　**DAY 31** 1.302 m.　　**DAY 32** 7.　　**DAY 33** 36 cm.

DAY 34 3 other ways. **DAY 35** 13. **DAY 36** 53. **DAY 37** they are parallel. **DAY 38** 5.940099.

DAY 39 19. **DAY 40** Australian. **DAY 41** 5 %, $\frac{1}{5}$, 0.5. **DAY 42** 2.98 and 5.98. **DAY 43** 5 cm^2.

DAY 44 10. **DAY 45** 0. **DAY 46** 958. **DAY 47** the reading test. **DAY 48** 67p (to nearest 1p).

DAY 49 46. **DAY 50** it weighs more than 180 g. **DAY 51** for example, 21 (or 22, 26, ...).

DAY 52 2 °C. **DAY 53** 13. **DAY 54** A. **DAY 55** 14 grams or (possibly) 13 grams. **DAY 56** 47.

DAY 57 2691. **DAY 58** seconds in a day. **DAY 59** 200. **DAY 60** mean. **DAY 61** P. **DAY 62** 1.

DAY 63 44. **DAY 64** (8, 5). **DAY 65** 96. **DAY 66** $\frac{1}{200}$. **DAY 67** yes. **DAY 68** Emmy's.

DAY 69 less than 115°. **DAY 70** 11 256. **DAY 71** 20 units. **DAY 72** more than 3.

DAY 73 6, 22, 33. **DAY 74** 0.16 years. **DAY 75** 48, 49, 50. **DAY 76** for example, $\frac{3}{10}$.

DAY 77 9 pm. **DAY 78** A. **DAY 79** 12. **DAY 80** yes. **DAY 81** 10 lb. **DAY 82** 1.04 cm.

DAY 83 Sherri. **DAY 84** 1°. **DAY 85** 3. **DAY 86** $\frac{1}{100}$. **DAY 87** X. **DAY 88** 50.

DAY 89 21 years 2 months. **DAY 90** 2. **DAY 91** 21 ÷ 5. **DAY 92** yes (see diagram).